CHRISTMAS CRAFTS
FOR CHILDREN

Written by Brenda Apsley
Illustrated by Lynn Aldous

STUDIO PUBLICATIONS
IPSWICH, ENGLAND

CONTENTS

BEFORE YOU BEGIN...

This book is packed full of ideas for making Christmas gifts, cards and decorations. There are step-by-step instructions and colour illustrations for each different project.

The craft ideas are meant to be good fun to try out . . . but there's nothing funny about something that doesn't turn out as it should, or — worse still — making a mess and getting into trouble! So, have a read through these few tips BEFORE YOU BEGIN!

★ **Read through the instructions from start to finish before getting to work with pens, scissors and the rest. If there's something that doesn't seem to make sense, or you aren't sure about, ask someone else.**

★ **Collect all the things you need. No good discovering you've run out of paint halfway through the craft making!**

★ **Spread old newspapers on tables and worktops before you begin — and clear away any mess afterwards.**

★ **Some of these crafts involve using the oven. *Make sure that an adult is there to help you.***

★ **Use only non-toxic glue and round-ended safety scissors. If sharper scissors are needed, then get an adult to help you.**

★ **Even though you've made Mum a lovely present you won't be too popular if you've managed to ruin your best jumper! An apron could be handy, especially if there's lots of painting involved.**

PAPER PUDDINGS

1 Take your brown paper bag (about 16cm square). Scrunch up some newspaper into a pudding shape and put into the paper bag. Mould the bag into a good pudding shape. Secure the edges of the bag with sticky tape.

2 Paint the paper bag 'pudding' dark brown. It may need more than one coat of paint. When the pudding is dry, paint on lots of small black 'currants'. Leave to dry.

3 On a sheet of white paper, draw a shape like the one shown here, about 10cm across. Cut out neatly.

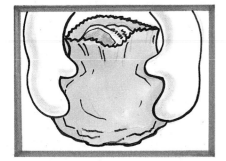

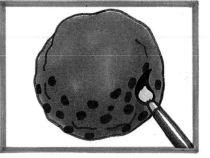

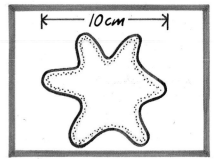

4 Put some glue around the edges on the WRONG side and stick to the top of the pudding. This is the white sauce dripping down the sides.

5 On green foil paper, draw some holly leaf shapes and cut out. They should be about 5cm long. Put a spot of glue at one end of five leaves and stick to the top of the pudding.

6 Cut out red foil squares about 3cm across. Roll them between your hands to make tiny round balls. Put a spot of glue on six 'berries' and stick them to the pudding, between the holly leaves.

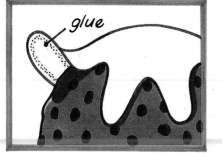

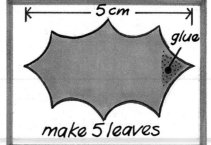

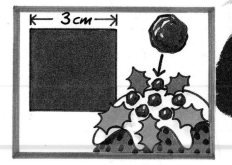

4

7 Draw a 20cm circle on white card and cut out. This is the plate for the pudding to sit on. Using felt tips, decorate the 'plate' with holly leaves and berries. Put some glue in the centre of the plate and press down the pudding firmly.

20 cm

Make a pudding for each Christmas dinner guest. If you like, make each guest's name a part of the plate design, and use as place cards. Make one big pudding (using the largest paper bag you can find) to sit in the centre of the table.

DAD DAD D

MUM MUM

CHRISTMAS CARDS

BOW BELLS CARD

You could make your own Christmas cards this year . . . they're cheap, easy — and fun.

you will need:

stiff card
pen
a paper punch

about 40cm of ribbon — gold, silver, tartan or Christmas-patterned about 1cm wide

1 Trace the bell template on this page. Use it to cut out two card bell shapes. With a paper punch, make a hole at the top of each bell.

2 Write your Christmas message on one bell. Put the plain bell on top, and thread the ribbon through the holes. Tie in a neat bow.

3 Leave the bow bells card plain, or decorate with gold and silver gummed paper shapes. Silver on black card looks good. Add glitter too, if you like.

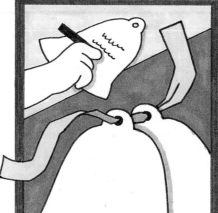

6

STAND-UP CARD

you will need:

stiff card — white or
coloured
felt tips
glitter

Can't draw? Even non-artists
can design a gift-wrapped
box and ribbon bow.
Remember to leave the top
of the bow intact, and add a
MERRY CHRISTMAS
message across the parcel.

1 Cut out a piece of card about
30cm × 12cm. Fold down
the centre, creasing firmly
with your thumb. The fold
should be at the top.

2 Working with the fold at the
top, use felt tips to design a
Christmas picture — perhaps
an angel (like the one shown
here) or a tree. Use your
imagination. Make the top
fold part of the design.

3 Cut out the shape, leaving a
part of the top fold intact,
and dot with glue. Sprinkle
on some glitter, shake off
excess, and the card is
ready to write and send.

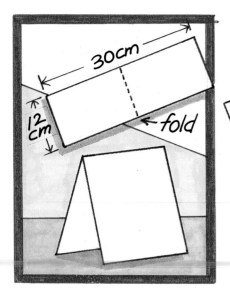

SPIRALS

you will need:

double-sided coloured foil
paper or thick kitchen foil
needle and cotton

* **Try making mini spirals
to hang from the tree,
using foil circles 8 or 9cm
across.**

1 Draw a circle about 30cm
across (a dinner plate is a
good guide). Cut out the
circle.

2 Using a pencil, draw a long
spiral line starting from the
centre of the circle and going
round and round until you
reach the outer edge.
CAREFULLY cut along the
line, starting from the outer
edge.

3 Make a knot in a length of
cotton, thread the needle,
and push through the centre
of the spiral. Tie in a hanging
loop.

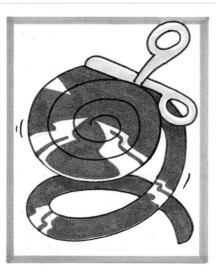

8

CONES

you will need:

double-sided coloured foil
paper or thick kitchen foil
needle and cotton

*** Make tiny cones to hang
from the tree, using circles
of foil about 10cm across.**

1 Draw a circle 30cm across
on the foil. Cut out.
Fold the circle in half. Then
make two more folds, as
shown in the illustration.

2 Working with the foil still
folded, make cuts across,
first from the left, then from
the right, and so on. The
cuts should be 2cm apart,
and should stop 1cm, from
the opposite edge. Make
cuts until you get to the base
of the cone.

3 Open out, then very carefully
pull and stretch the cone
down, taking care not to rip
the foil. Using knotted cotton
and a needle, make a
hanging loop at the tip of the
cone.

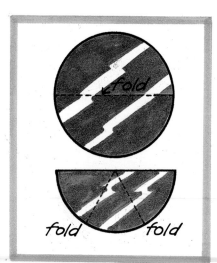

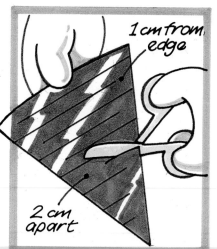

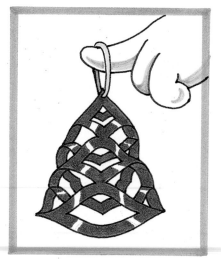

CLOCK CALENDAR

Move the calendar clock hands to point to the day, the date and the month. You can use it for any year.

you will need:

1 large white paper plate
3 pieces of card in red, yellow and blue
a paper fastener
Sellotape
a piece of string about 10cm long

1 Draw 4 circles on the plate, using compasses. If you don't have compasses, draw around plates, saucers and cups. Use different colour felt-tips for each circle. Leave the middle of the plate and the rim blank.

2 Using a felt tip, write the names of the months between the first and second circles. Space the months evenly, three in each quarter of the plate, starting with January at the top.

3 Using a felt tip, write the names of the days of the week between the second and third circles. Space them out as evenly as you can, starting with Monday at the top.

4 Using a blue felt tip, write the numbers 1 to 31 between the third and fourth circles. Space them out evenly, about 8 in each quarter, starting with 1 at the top.

5 Make three clock 'hands'. Cut a red strip 2cm wide and long enough to reach from the middle of the plate to the months. Cut a yellow strip long enough to reach the days and a blue strip to reach the dates. Cut each of the coloured hands to a point at one end.

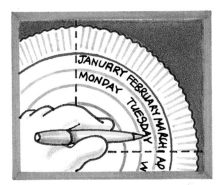

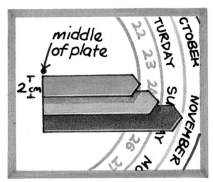

6 Make a hole at the flat end of each clock hand and thread them onto the paper fastener — blue first, then yellow, then red. Push the fastener through the middle of the plate and open it out at the back.

7 Decorate the rim of the clock calendar. Draw a design of bells, holly leaves and robins in felt tips, or draw a ring of snowmen.

8 On the back of the clock, make a loop of string, held in place by Sellotape. This makes a loop to hang the calendar on the wall.

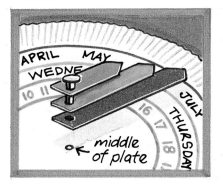

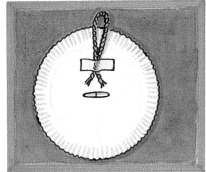

Every day, move the date and day hands on the clock calendar. Move the red hand at the start of each new month.

The clock calendar makes a great gift — why not make one for your parents?

SNOWFLAKES AND FROST

If you look at snowflakes through a microscope you'll see lovely patterns. Make some surprise paper snowflakes — you won't know what pattern you've made until you open them up.

you will need:

thin white paper
scissors
double-sided sticky tape

1 Cut out a square of paper measuring about 20cm on each side. Fold the paper square in half, then quarters. Fold once again to make a triangle shape.

2 Draw designs on the folded paper. Carefully cut away the coloured areas. Open out the snowflake.

3 Try some round snowflakes, too. Lay a saucer on a sheet of paper and draw around it. Cut out a paper circle. Fold in half, then again, then again, until you have a cone shape. Press the folds with your thumb.

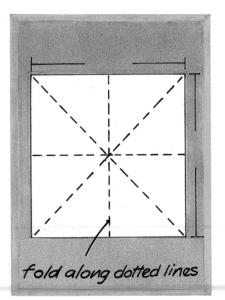

fold along dotted lines

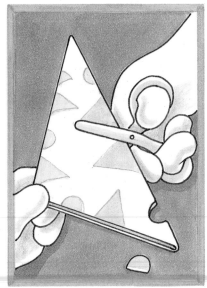

fold along dotted lines

4 Cut off the tip of the cone. Cut small notches in the sides and bottom edge, pulling away the cutout sections. Open out carefully.

5 Make lots and lots of paper snowflakes in different shapes and sizes. Using double-sided sticky tape, arrange them on a large sheet of red paper and pin to the wall, or use the snowflakes to decorate Christmas cards. Snowflakes look good on windows, too — just stick them on with double-sided tape.

Try painting snowflake and frost patterns on windows. They look good with light shining through them — and they will wash off after Christmas!

you will need:

shoe whitener in a bottle (the kind sold for gym shoes)
a small paintbrush

1 For frost patterns, fill your brush with whitener and make short strokes, some up, some across, like this.

2 Use shoe whitener and your fingers to make a jolly snowstorm. Just dip your forefinger in whitener and press it all over the window glass in a random pattern.

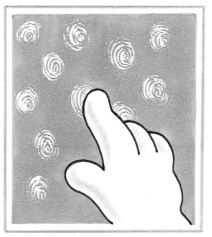

13

CHAINS

PAPER CHAINS

1 Cut out lots and lots of gummed paper rectangles 20cm × 3cm. Choose Christmassy colours like red, green and white.

2 Wet one end of a rectangle and join to the other end to make a circle. Thread another rectangle through the first circle, wet, and stick. Carry on making interlocking rings until you have a long chain.

3 Hang from walls using drawing pins or sticky tabs. Make a tiny paper chain to hang from the tree, using silver and gold paper rectangles 1cm × 5cm.

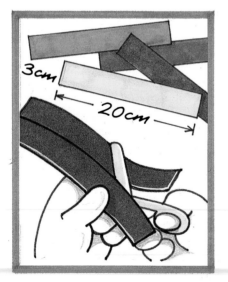

CUT PAPER CHAINS I

1 Cut out a strip of paper 15cm wide and as long as you like — paper cut from a roll is ideal. If your paper strip is not long enough, use sticky tape to stick lengths together.

2 Using scissors, make cuts along one side of the paper, 12cm long and 12cm apart.

3 On the other side of the strip make more cuts in the middle of the first lot, 12cm long and 12cm apart. Pull the paper gently to loosen the chain.

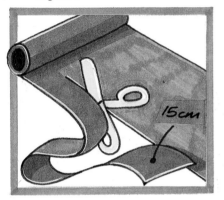

CUT PAPER CHAINS II

1 Cut out a strip of paper 16cm wide and as long as possible, joining lengths of paper if necessary.

2 Fold in half along the length of the paper. Make cuts along one side of the paper, 6cm long and 12cm apart.

3 Make more cuts on the other side in the middle of the first, 6cm long and 12cm apart. Pull the chain apart gently.

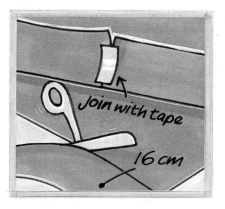

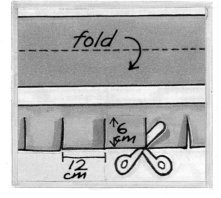

SANTA CANDLE LIGHTS

These glass candle holders are simple to make — and look great lit up on a dark winter's night.

you will need:

clear glass jars (coffee, jam or honey jars are good)
enamel craft paints

night lights (in packs from hardware shops)
paintbrushes

1 Wash the glass jar very carefully. Soak off the label. Rinse, and dry.
Fill a paintbrush with white enamel paint and cover the bottom of the jar. Paint the INSIDE only. This is snow.

2 Fill a paintbrush with red enamel and paint a Santa Claus figure — arms, legs and body. Paint on the OUTSIDE of the jar.

3 Using white enamel, paint Santa's head. Paint in his eyes, nose and mouth in black. Finish him off with a red hat.

7 If you like, you can decorate the stocking with scrap felt shapes. Just cut out holly leaves, bells, snowmen or stars and glue in place.

...AND SMALL

1 Using the diagram again, cut out another stocking shape — but this time on a grid where each square measures 1cm. Your stocking will be 9 or 10cm long. Cut out two felt stockings.

2 Cut out a piece of white felt 2cm wide and 11cm long. Glue the stockings together, as before, and the white band around the top.

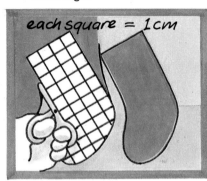

Using the squared pattern here, you can make all sizes of stocking. For tiny stockings, draw out 1cm squares on your paper; for jumbo stockings, draw out 6cm squares.

Give the small stockings as little gifts, with a wrapped chocolate or bath beads inside. Make a loop with needle and thread and hang them from the tree, too.

MARZIPAN MAKES

1 Preheat the oven to gas mark 5/180°C/350°F. Line a baking tray with kitchen foil. Divide the block of marzipan into three. With VERY clean hands, put the first third on a worktop or board lightly sprinkled with icing sugar. Knead the marzipan until smooth.

2 Put one or two drops of red food colouring on the second piece of marzipan and knead to spread the colour. Mix green colouring into the third piece of marzipan. Use food colouring carefully — a little goes a long way.

you will need:

a packet of marzipan
bottles of red and green
natural food colouring
icing sugar
small shaped biscuit
cutters
rolling pin
a baking tray lined with
kitchen foil

to decorate: a tube of
ready to pipe icing, tiny
edible silver balls,
hundreds and thousands

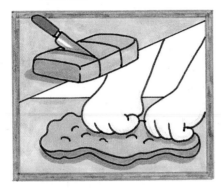

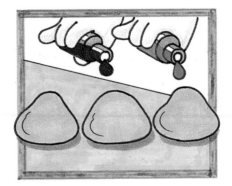

3 Roll out each block of marzipan on a board lightly dusted with icing sugar. Roll evenly until the marzipan is about as thick as a 50p piece.

4 Using small biscuit cutters, stamp out Christmas shapes like trees, bells and stars. If you don't have any cutters, use a knife to cut around simple card templates — hearts and Christmas stockings are easy shapes to draw.

5 Carefully (a palette knife is useful) lift the shapes onto the baking tray. Put into the oven and cook for 5 minutes ONLY, until they are set. Take out wearing oven gloves and leave to cool.

6 These marzipan shapes will keep for about two weeks, stored in a dry place.

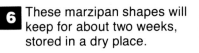

NUTTY LOGS

you will need:

a packet of marzipan
50g flaked almonds
egg white, beaten
pastry brush

1 Using your fingers like a rolling pin, roll the marzipan into a long sausage shape about 3cm across. Cut into 'logs' about 8cm long.

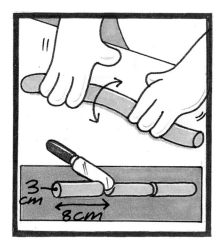

7 To decorate, 'draw' simple designs using the piping nozzle on the tube of icing, or write HAPPY XMAS. Put icing dots all over the shapes and press a silver ball into each one while still soft, or press on multicoloured hundreds and thousands.

2 Spread out the flaked almonds on a plate and put them under a hot grill for a few minutes, until toasted. Watch them carefully — they soon burn. Chop quite finely.

3 Brush the logs with a little beaten egg white and roll the sides in the chopped, toasted almonds. Leave the ends uncovered.
Leave for a few hours to dry out — then eat!

FUN WITH FOIL

SHINY ICICLES

you will need:

double-sided foil craft
paper
a wooden spoon
metallic thread

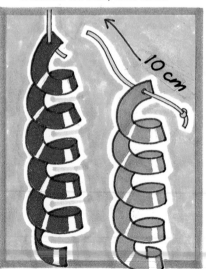

**Foil icicles look good hung
from the branches of a
Christmas tree. Make lots
to hang from every branch.**

1 Cut out lots of rectangles of foil paper 2cm wide and 30cm long.

2 Wind each foil strip tightly around the handle of a wooden spoon.

3 Gently, slip out the wooden spoon, leaving the foil icicle behind. Make a hole in one end of the foil, thread through a 10cm piece of metallic thread, and knot.

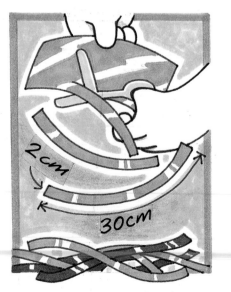

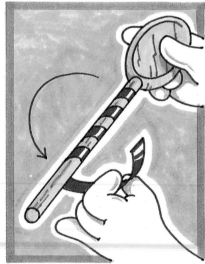

FOIL BALLS

1 Cut out lots of squares of kitchen foil 12cm × 12cm. Gently scrunch up the foil squares into loose round balls. Try to make neat, even shapes.

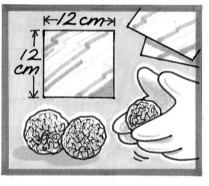

2 Make a knot in the end of a length of thread and push the needle through from one side of a foil ball to the other. Tie the long end in a hanging loop.

Hang the foil balls from the branches of a Christmas tree.

FOIL GARLAND

you will need:

kitchen foil
needle and strong thread

1 Cut out lots of foil squares in three different sizes: 12cm, 18cm and 24cm. Scrunch them into balls, as before.

2 Knot the end of a long length of strong thread and push the needle through first a small ball, then a medium ball, finally a large ball. Repeat until you have made a very long garland to hang on the tree or around a room.

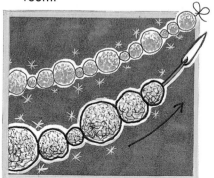

CARD  TREE

you will need:

green card	silver foil paper or kitchen
brown card	foil
red card	paper punch
gold foil paper	sticky pads or tabs

1 Cut out three green card triangles: one with sides 75cm long; one with sides 65cm long; one with sides 55cm long.
* If you don't have green card, use any colour and paint it, leaving it to dry before you go on to the next step.

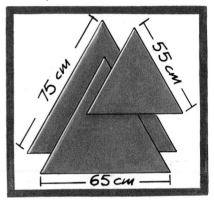

5 Make a star for the top of the tree. Cut out two gold foil triangles with sides of 10cm. Put a little glue in the middle of one triangle and press the other triangle on top, making a six-point star. Glue the star to the top of the tree.

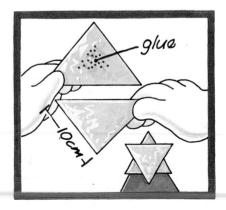

2 Lay the biggest triangle flat, and spread some glue across the top point. Press the middle-sized triangle on top. Glue the second point, and press down the smallest triangle, as in the illustration. You have made the basic Christmas tree.

3 Cut out a tree trunk using dark brown card (or painting white card). It should be 12cm wide and 15cm long. Put some glue along the top edge of the trunk and press it firmly in place on the BACK of the tree.

4 Cut out a tub shape in red card (or red-painted card). It should be about 22cm wide at the top, 15cm at the bottom, and about 15cm high. Cut slanted sides. Glue on the bottom edge of the tree trunk.

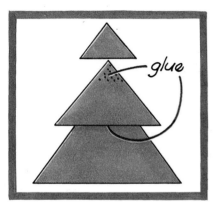

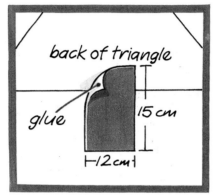

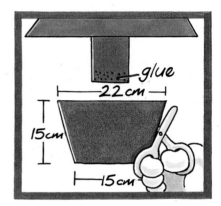

6 Make some candles. Cut six red card rectangles 3cm wide and 12 cm long. Cut six flame shapes from gold foil paper. Stick a flame to the top of each candle. Glue one candle to the end of each tree branch.

7 Using a paper punch, cut lots of holes in silver paper or kitchen foil. Put a little glue on the back of each paper circle and dot them all over the tree.

8 Use sticky tabs to fix the Christmas tree to the wall. Use the same tabs to stick your Christmas cards onto the tree. The cards will be shown off to good effect.

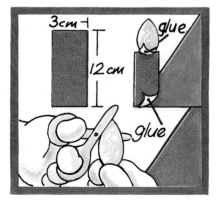

DINNER TABLE DECORATION

you will need:

thin white card
thick red and green
felt tips
metallic silver or gold felt
tip
glue
fine black felt tip

Stand a tree in front of
each place at the
Christmas dinner table, so
everyone knows where to
sit. Make more trees
(without names) and use as
decorations.

1 Cut out a piece of card 15 ×
12cm. Fold in half.

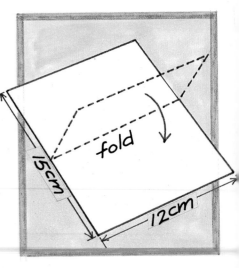

2 Using a pencil, copy the half-tree shape shown here onto the card. The fold should be in the middle of the tree. Cut out. This is your tree and tub 'pattern'.

3 Using the 'pattern' tree, draw and cut out lots more tree shapes in card. You will need four for each place card.

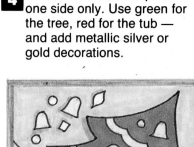

4 Colour each tree shape on one side only. Use green for the tree, red for the tub — and add metallic silver or gold decorations.

5 Using a black felt tip, write each guest's name on four tubs.

6 Fold each tree shape in half down the middle, coloured sides together. Make neat, sharp creases.

fold

7 Put some glue on the backs of four tree shapes. Press together to make a cross. Match the shapes carefully, especially the bases of the tubs.

PAPER, RIBBONS AND BOWS

Gift wrapping makes any gift look extra special. Here are some ideas for wrapping paper, ribbons and bows.

SNOWFLAKE PAPER

you will need:

plain, dark-coloured paper
a small paper doily
white or silver paint

paintbrush
sticky tape

1 Lay the doily on the paper. Hold in place with a tiny piece of sticky tape. Fill your brush with paint and cover the whole of the doily filling in all the spaces. Do not paint beyond the edge.

2 When dry, lift off the doily carefully to reveal the snowflake pattern. Repeat to fill the paper. To save time, use lots of doilys and paint at the same time.

FOIL BOW

you will need:

**foil sequin waste (from sewing shops and haberdashers)
sticky tape
metallic string tie**

1 Cut a 26cm length of sequin waste (the bits left after sequins have been stamped out). Mark the middle and fold in the two ends, as in the diagram. Secure with a small piece of sticky tape.

2 Pinch the middle into a bow shape and tie, using metallic tie. Fix to gift-wrapped parcel using sticky pads or double-sided tape.

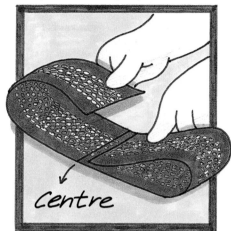

CURLY RIBBONS

Wrap your gift and tie with a very narrow curling ribbon, leaving ends 60cm long. Pull one blade of a pair of round-ended scissors firmly down the lengths of ribbon. The ribbon will fall into tight curls.

POMPONS

you will need:

balls or part balls of
knitting wool
empty yoghurt or cream
carton
5p piece
card

1 Draw a circle on the card, using the base of the yoghurt or cream carton as a guide. Put a 5p piece in the middle and draw around it. Repeat. Cut out two card circles, then cut away the middle, making rings.

2 Choose your wool. Christmassy colours like bright red, green and white look good, plus metallic silver. Use all the same colour, or knot together 2 metre strips for a random look. Holding the two card rings together, wind the wool around until the card is covered and there is no space left in the centre.

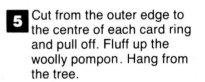

3 With scissors, cut through all thicknesses of wool at the outer edge.

4 Cut off a 1 metre length of matching wool and slip it between the two card rings. Pull, then tie firmly, knotting the ends together to make a loop.

5 Cut from the outer edge to the centre of each card ring and pull off. Fluff up the woolly pompon. Hang from the tree.

TOPPERS

you will need:

foil milk bottle tops, carefully washed and dried

needle and thread

Hang foil stars all over the tree, or thread lots of stars onto a long piece of cotton (through the centres) and hang as a garland.

BELLS

1 Flatten out each foil top. Put your forefinger in the centre of each top. With your other hand, mould the foil down over your finger, making a bell shape.

2 Knot a length of cotton thread and push up through the bell. Tie in a hanging loop.

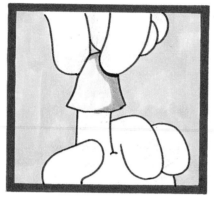

STARS

1 Flatten out each foil top. Make eight cuts in each top, evenly spaced and about 12mm long.

2 Hold each 'arm' between finger and thumb and twist, as in the illustration.

3 Tie a knot at one end of the cotton and thread the needle. Push through the edge of one of the side 'arms'. Tie a loop at the end of the cotton.

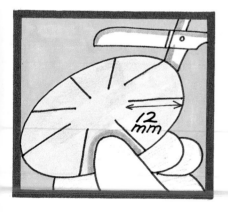

ADVENT CALENDAR

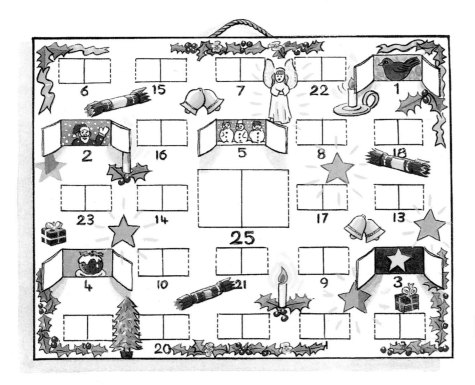

Open a new numbered window each day in December.

1 On one sheet of paper or card use a pencil and ruler to draw 24 small rectangles, 4cm × 2cm. Draw a bigger rectangle in the middle of the paper, 6cm × 4cm.

2 Carefully, make three cuts through each rectangle — one along the top and bottom lines and one down the middle. If you need sharp scissors for this, get help from a grown-up. Fold back the uncut lines. You now have 25 'windows' that can be opened and closed.

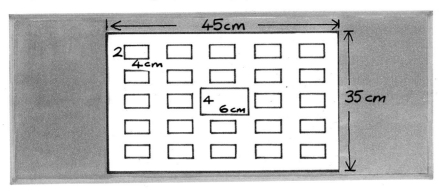

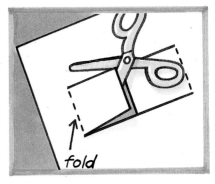

36

3 Turn the sheet of paper over and, on the WRONG side, put a line of glue around the edge. Put the plain piece of paper on top of the window sheet. Press and leave the glue to dry.

4 Cut tiny 'pictures' from the old Christmas cards and wrapping paper. Choose a robin, gifts, a stocking, a cake, holly, an angel — anything to do with Christmas. Cut out 24 pictures 4cm × 2cm and one bigger picture, 6cm × 4cm — perhaps a nativity scene.

5 Put some glue on the back of each little picture and stick one in each 'window'. Trim them if they don't quite fit. Put the bigger picture in the middle window. Close up all the 'windows' so the pictures are hidden.

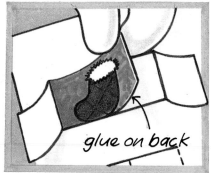

6 Using a medium felt tip pen, write a number under each window, from 1 to 24. Number the bigger window 25. Number them in order, or dot them around — whichever you like.

7 Decorate the calendar with coloured felt tip pens. Draw on simple Christmas symbols — holly leaves and berries, stars, bells and Christmas trees. If you don't like drawing, glue on some more cut-out Christmas pictures.

8 Take a piece of thin string about 10cm long and Sellotape it to the middle of the back of the calendar. Now you can hang up your calendar.

NOVELTY CARDS

you will need:

stiff white card
green and red felt tips

POP-UP CHRISTMAS TREE

1 Cut out a piece of card about 30cm × 20cm. Fold down the middle, pressing the fold firmly.

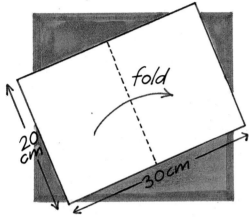

2 Draw dotted lines like this. Cut along the lines.

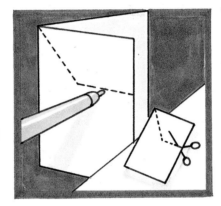

3 Fold down the point like this. Crease the fold firmly.

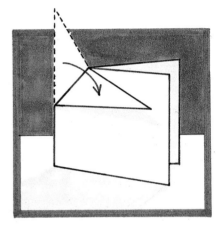

4 Lift up the point and fold it again, this time on the INSIDE of the card.

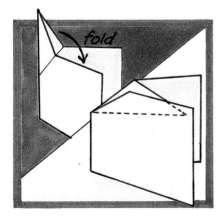

5 Open out the card. Colour the tree triangle green, and add a red base. Refold the top of the tree so that when the card is opened, it pops up.

6 Write HAPPY CHRISTMAS in red and green felt tips on the outside.

CRACKER CARD

you will need:

stiff card, white or coloured
felt tips

1 Cut out a piece of card 42cm × 10cm. Using a pencil and ruler, lightly mark 5 lines, 7cm apart.

2 Make 4 folds down the card, like this. Press them firmly. Rub out the pencil lines.

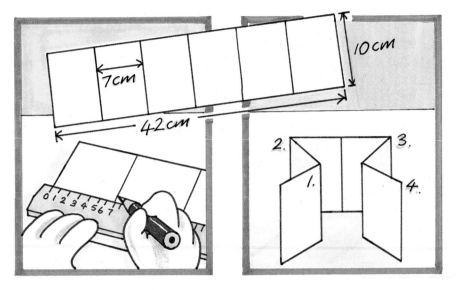

3 Close up the card and, using bright felt tips, draw a big cracker across the centre folds.

4 Open up the card. Continue the cracker up to the next folds. Make the ends jagged, as if it has been pulled.

5 In the middle section of the card, write your message — how about HAVE A CRACKING CHRISTMAS? Refold the card.

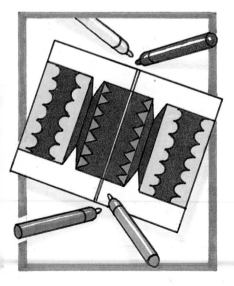

POMANDERS 'N' PUDS

Gifts are extra-special when you've taken the time and trouble to make them yourself. Here are some easy ideas.

These 'puddings' will help make drawers and wardrobes smell sweet. So will pomanders, which were used hundreds of years ago to ward off bad smells. Now their spicy-sweet smell will fill a room.

ORANGE POMANDERS

you will need:

oranges
a packet of whole cloves

about 1.5m ribbon, 1cm wide
dressmaking pins

1 Push cloves (stalk end first) into the orange, covering the whole fruit tightly, or making straight lines. If you find it difficult to push in the cloves, make holes first with a skewer or knitting needle — CAREFULLY. A bowl of these basic pomanders looks and smells great.

2 For hanging pomanders cut out two pieces of ribbon. Measure around the orange. Cut the first piece of ribbon this measurement plus 1cm; cut the second piece of ribbon this measurement plus 1 metre. For example, if your orange measures 20cm, your ribbon pieces should be 21cm and 1 metre 20cm.

measure orange

3 Put the short ribbon around the orange, pull tight and pin in place.

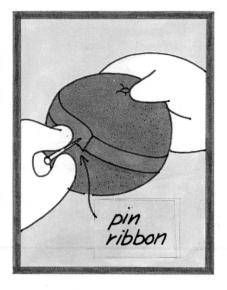

pin ribbon

4 Pin on the longer piece of ribbon at right angles to the first, leaving the end free. Double back and pin the end in place, making a long loop.

5 Stud the orange with cloves as before, and hang in wardrobes — or on the Christmas tree.

POT POURRI PUDDINGS

you will need:

**a handful of pot pourri
a pretty lace-edged or embroidered hankie
.5 metre of 1cm wide ribbon — maybe tartan or velvet
small elastic band**

1 Put a handful of pot pourri in the middle of the hankie. Gather up the edges and make the pot pourri into a tight ball. Hold in place with a small elastic band.

elastic band

2 Tie the ribbon around the neck of the pudding in a neat bow, or knot and tie the ends to make a hanging loop. Frill out the edges of the hankie.

DOVES
OF PEACE

you will need:

stiff white card
double-sided foil wrapping
paper — silver and gold
look effective

black felt tip
needle
invisible thread (or fine
white cotton)

1 Cut out a piece of card 18cm × 12cm. Using a pencil and ruler, divide it into 2cm squares.

2 Using the design here as a guide, draw the dove shape on your card square by square. Mark the position of beak, eye, hole and rectangle.

3 Cut out the dove shape carefully. This first dove is your pattern — use it to cut out more doves, drawing around it.

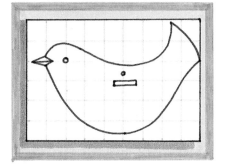

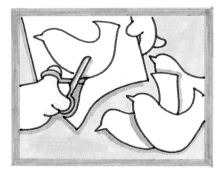

4 Using a black felt tip, draw beaks and eyes on each dove. Remember to draw on each side of the card.

5 Using a pencil, mark the position of the hole and rectangle on each dove. Ask a grown-up to cut out the thin rectangle. It is 1.5cm long.

6 Make the wings. Cut out a rectangle of paper for each dove 30cm × 18cm. Make sharp pleats in the paper, creasing the folds firmly and neatly. Each pleat should be 2cm wide.

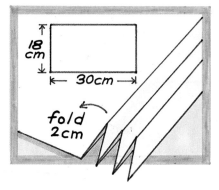

7 Holding the folded paper, slip it through the cut-out rectangle. When both sides are equal, fan out the pleats. Where the wings meet under the bird's body, apply a dab of glue and hold in place until dry.

8 Thread a length of invisible thread through the needle. Knot one end and push the needle through the hole in front of the dove's wings.

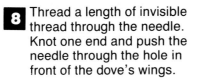

Hang the doves of peace from a Christmas tree, strung along broad ribbon across a room, or at the window. Or hang them from a silver tinsel-covered metal coathanger as a mobile.

CHRISTMAS TREE GARLANDS

Christmas tree decorations that you can eat!

POPCORN CHAINS

1 First pop the popcorn kernels. Get a grown up to help with this. You can buy popcorn to pop in a lidded pan, or special microwave popcorn. Follow the directions on the packet carefully. Leave the popped corn to cool.

2 Thread the needle. Make a large knot at one end of the cotton thread. Carefully push the needle through the pieces of popcorn. When your garland is long enough, knot the end of the thread.

Variations:
Use poster paints to paint the popcorn chains in Christmassy colours. Colour the whole chain red, or colour each piece of popcorn for a multicoloured garland. DO NOT EAT PAINTED POPCORN.

Hang the popcorn chains across the branches of your Christmas tree. Victorian children living about a hundred years ago used to make garlands just like these.

44

SWEET CHAINS

you will need:

lots of wrapped sweets —
those wrapped in coloured
foil and transparent paper
are ideal
large needle
strong thread

Buy packets of toffee-
coated ready-popped
popcorn and thread them
into a garland as before.
Handle with care — this
garland will be very sticky!

1 Make a knot at one end of
the thread. Thread the
needle and carefully push it
through the twisted wrapping
paper.

2 When all the sweets
are threaded, knot the end of
the cotton. Hang the garland
from the tree.

3 To make the sweets into a
longer garland, thread them
like this: down through one
end of the sweet wrapping,
across the back, and up
through the other end. The
sweets will lie end to end.

45

SALT PASTRY MAKES

Salt pastry is a good modelling dough that is very easy to make and work with. It is made with flour, salt and water — but remember, it is NOT edible.

you will need:

2 cups plain flour
1 cup salt
1 cup water

1 Using a cup, measure the flour and salt into a bowl. Mix, then add the water. Stir with a fork until you have a firm dough. Knead the mixture for about five minutes until it is smooth. The pastry should look like putty.

CANDLE HOLDERS

you will need:

1 quantity salt pastry	**candles**
paints or felt tips	**paint brushes**
polyurethane varnish	**rolling pin**

1 Preheat the oven at 180°C/350°F/gas mark 4. Roll out the pastry to a thickness of about 4cm, and cut out shapes as before. If you prefer, mould the holders in your hands — a smooth ball makes an easy Christmas pudding or snowball.

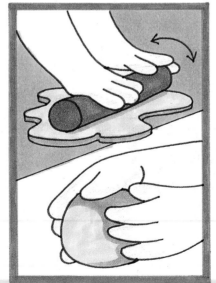

2 Press a candle into the middle of each holder, pressing it almost to the base. Remove. Put on a baking tray and cook for one hour. Leave to cool. Later, decorate and varnish as with the tree decorations.

CHRISTMAS TREE DECORATIONS

you will need:

1 quantity salt pastry
biscuit cutters
paints or felt tips
polyurethane varnish

rolling pin
fine ribbon or gift tie
paint brushes

1 Preheat the oven at 180°C/350°F/gas mark 4. Get adult help. Roll out the pastry evenly. It should be about .5cm thick. Using Christmassy cutters (bells, trees, holly leaves etc) press out lots of shapes. If you don't have cutters, get help to cut out simple shapes using a butter knife.

2 Use a thin skewer or cocktail stick to make a hole at the top of each shape. Put the shapes on a baking tray and cook for an hour. When light golden brown they are ready. Take out of the oven CAREFULLY and leave to cool.

3 Paint or felt tip the shapes and leave to dry. Later, cover with a coat of varnish. When dry, thread a short length of ribbon or gift tie through each hanging hole, and knot the ends together. Hang from the tree or in a window.

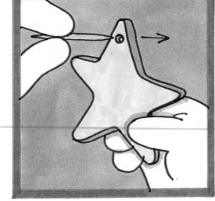

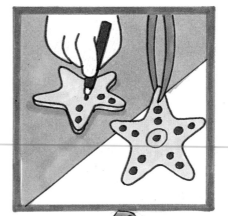

A candle in front of each guest looks good. For a table centre, mould a fat ring of clay, wetting the edges to join. Use candles to make five evenly-spaced holes and bake and decorate as before.

PAPER LANTERN

1 Cut out two paper rectangles, one 25cm × 16cm, the other 20cm × 2cm.

2 Fold the large rectangle in half. Cutting from the folded edge, make lots of cuts 6cm long and 2cm apart.

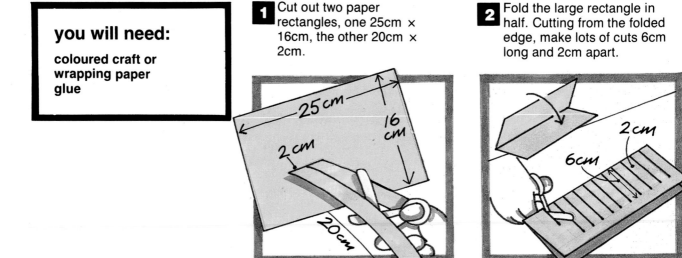

3 Open out the paper and glue the edges together to make the lantern shape.

4 Glue each end of the long paper strip to the lantern to make a handle.

5 Dab on a little glue and sprinkle on some glitter for extra sparkle. Red cellophane paper looks good scrunched up inside the lantern. It shows through the slits as if the lantern is lit.

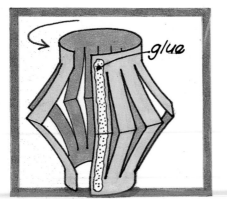